Printed and published in Great Britain by D. C. THOMSON & Co., Ltd., 185 Fleet Street, London, EC4A 2HS.
© D. C. THOMSON & CO., LTD., 1982.
ISBN 0 85116 245 2

RIKKI
The Rickshaw Boy

RIKKI HOY needed strong lungs and sturdy limbs for his job. He was a rickshaw boy in a town in Malaya. It was sometimes a lonely job, and for the sake of company, Rikki had a big monkey for a pet — a gibbon called Kong.

Kong usually travelled on the rickshaw too when Rikki had a passenger, like today when the boy was ferrying an important looking business man to the railway station. They were all unaware that three men in a big car were following them.

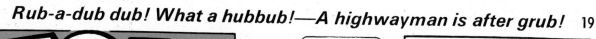

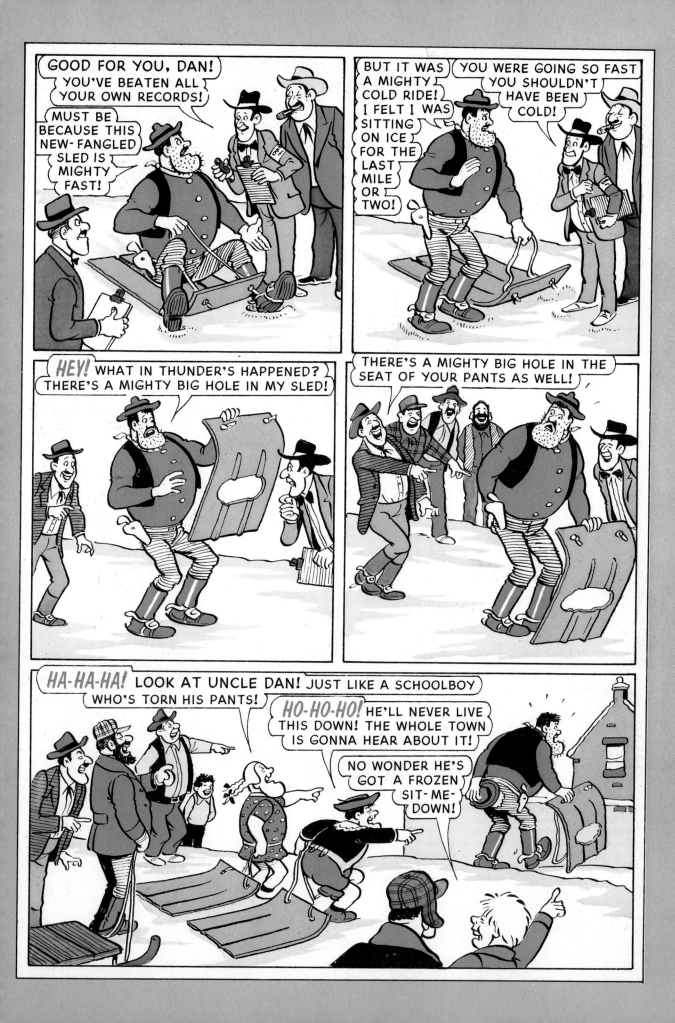

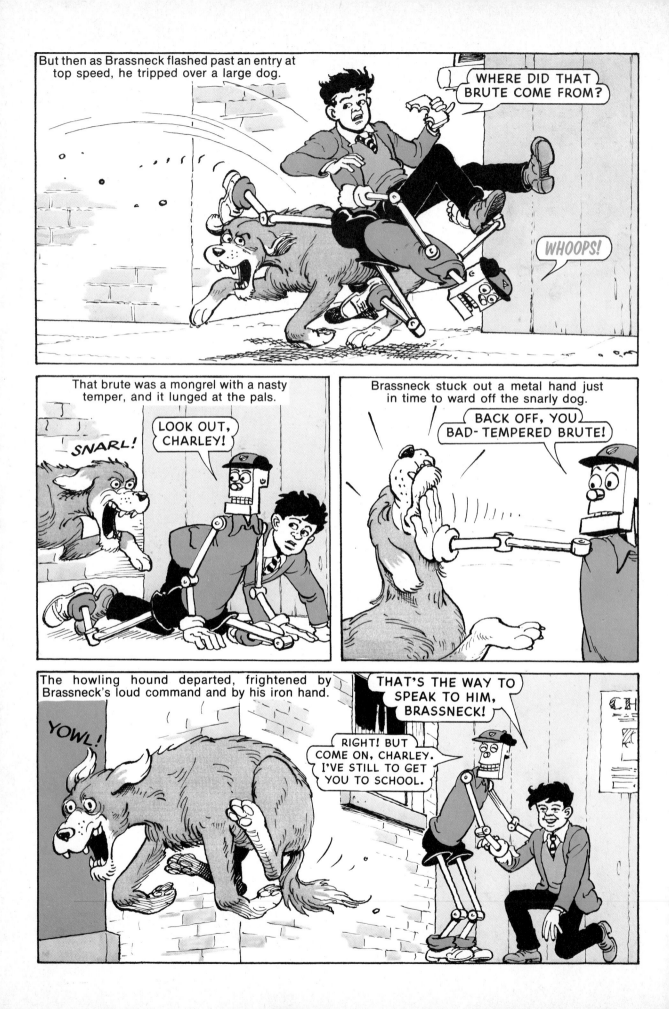

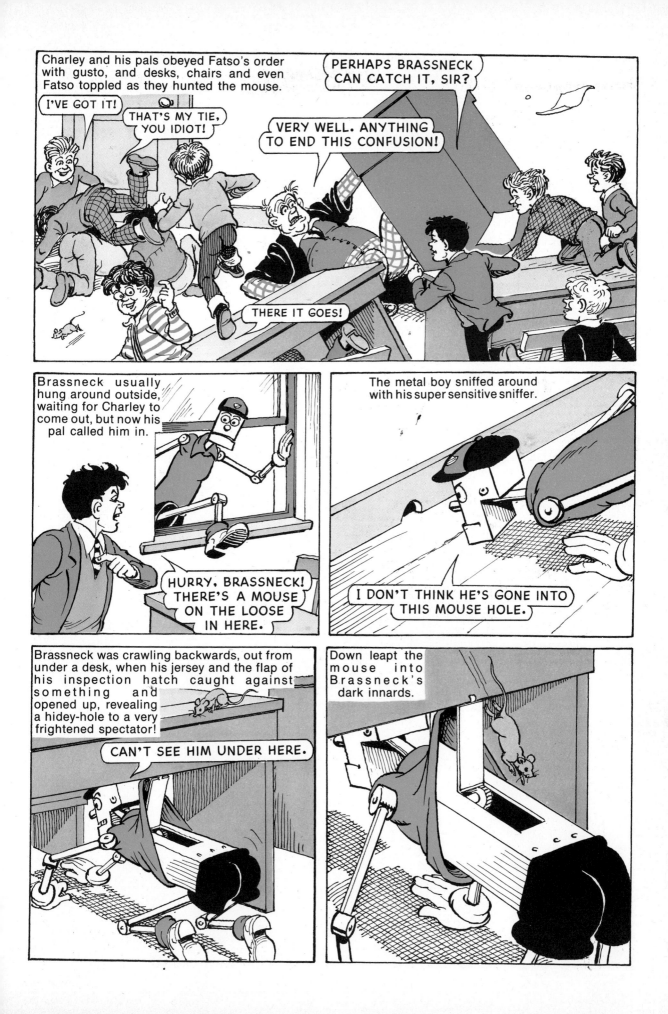

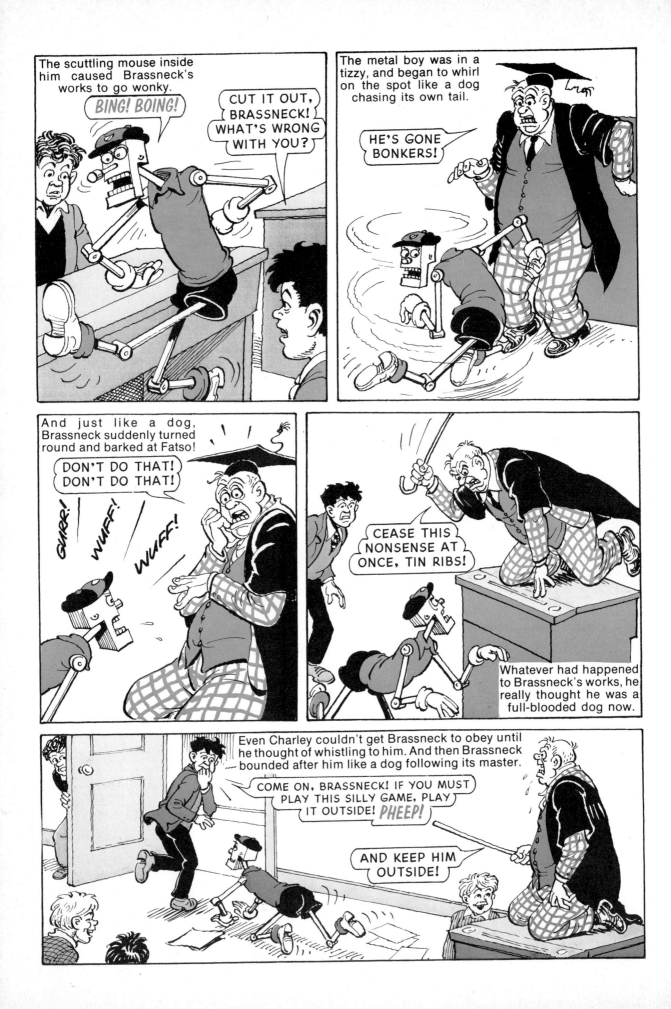

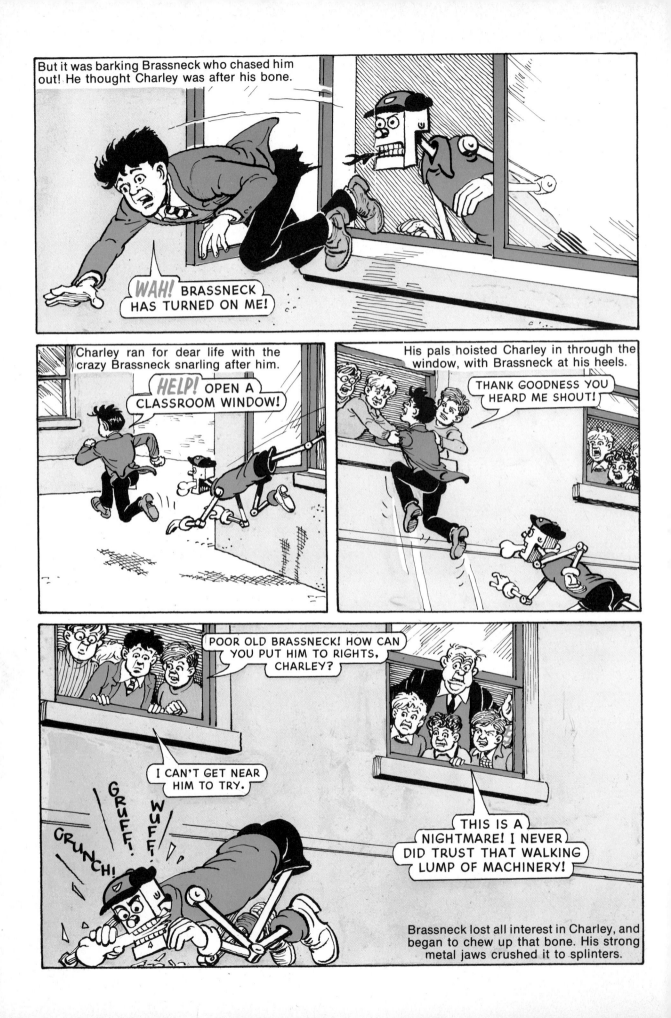

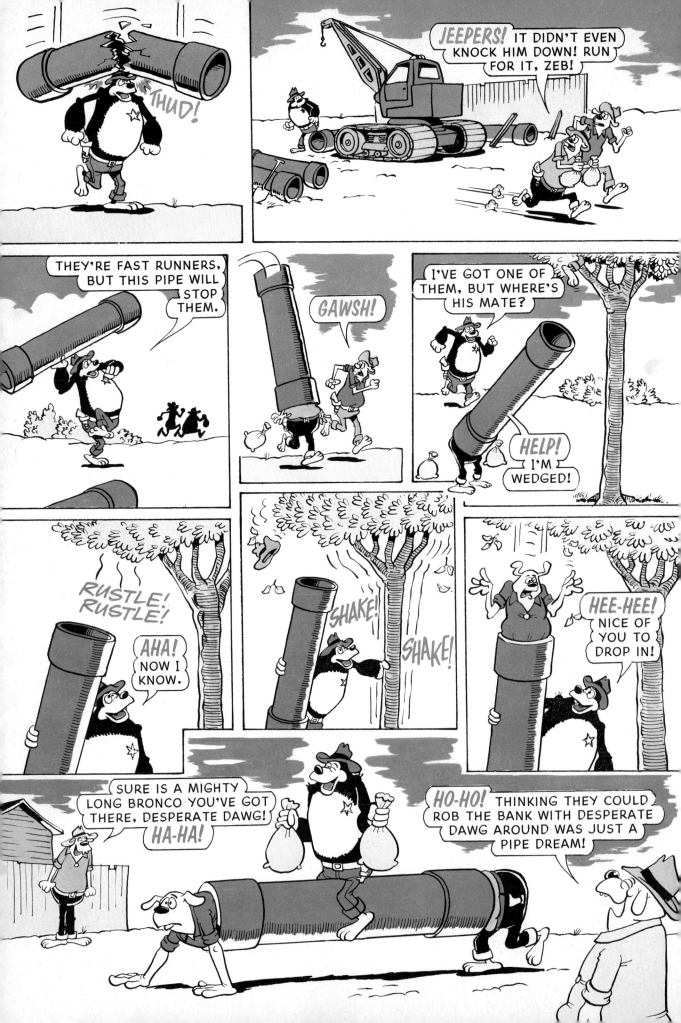

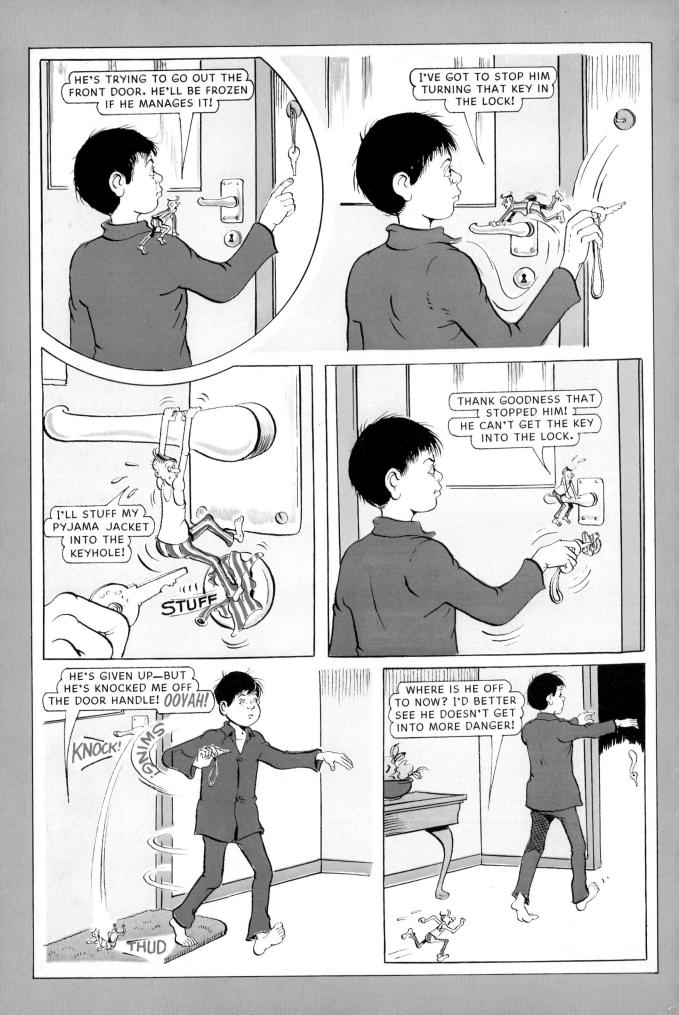

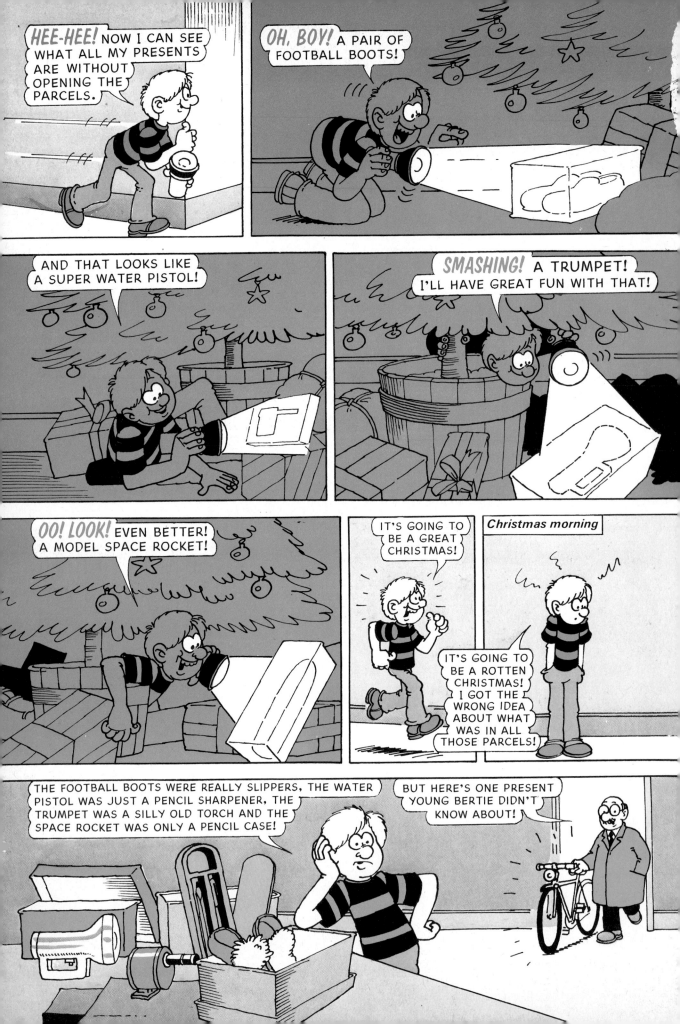

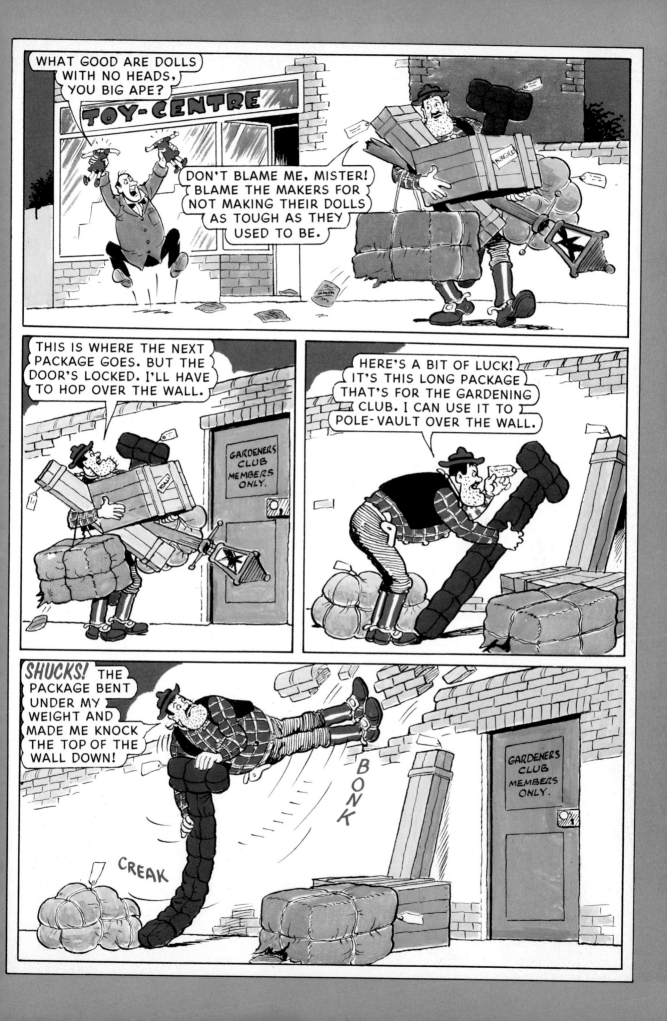

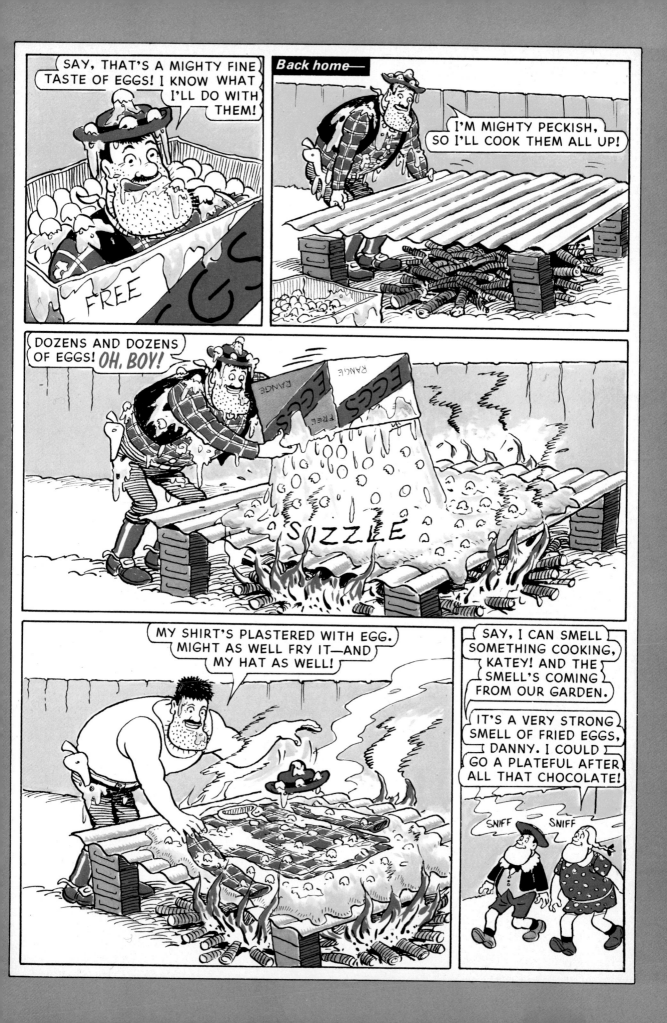

GEORDIE JESTERY

JACK SILVER

JACK SILVER lived in the weird world of Marsuvia, away in Outer Space, where most things were done by machinery. All the amazing machines you could think of were in use here — and so were some you could never think of in a hundred years! As Jack waited to meet Curly Perkins, his visitor from Earth, he bought ice cream from a robot.

Little did Jack know then that before long he would be locked in a desperate struggle with the Space bandit, Captain Zapp, the most wanted man in Marsuvia.

ONE LARGE ICE-CREAM, PLEASE, AND DON'T GO AWAY. MY PAL WILL PROBABLY WANT ONE WHEN HE GETS HERE IN A FEW MINUTES.

BEEP! AS YOU WISH, YOUNG SIR! PLACE YOUR MONEY IN MY RIGHT MITT, PLEASE! BEEP!

CAPTAIN ZAPP

With Captain Zapp out of the way, the boys had another look at his marvellous clock.

PITY IT HAS STOPPED WORKING NOW, JACK!

MAYBE WE COULD GET IT GOING AGAIN, THOUGH!

Jack made some alterations inside and carried in a new cylinder of gas.

WHAT'S THAT FOR, JACK?

YOU'LL SEE!

The clock was started up again — and it proved to be a great attraction for all Marsuvians. But instead of knockout gas, the hoses now sprayed happy gas over the crowd!

ROAR!

CLANG!

WHOOSH!

MAYBE THEY'LL LET CAPTAIN ZAPP OFF THE WORST OF HIS PUNISHMENT FOR PUTTING UP SUCH A MARVELLOUS FUN CLOCK!